C000094982

The library of
Stable Management

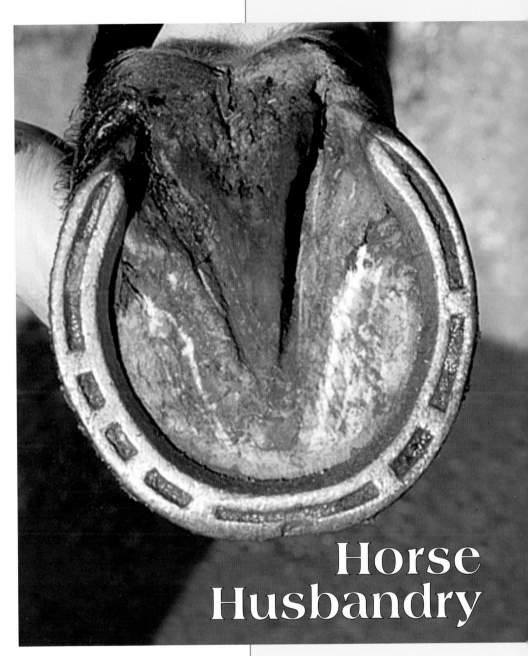

Horse
Husbandry

Mark Hallion
and Julie Langrish

The library of Stable Management
Horse Husbandry

Contents

The authors would like to thank the following for their help:
- Malcolm Dunning Saddlery
- Jeremy Mantell MRCVS
- Mrs. Gillian Knight and Mrs. Yvonne Bryant for modelling

Chapter One

General care

Before buying your horse you have to have somewhere safe and suitable to keep it.

Depending on what sort of horse you have, the minimum you will need is good grazing and a field shelter. The amount of time the horse spends in the field is determined by what type of horse it is, the work it will be doing and how much time you have to look after it.

If your horse is one of the hardy breeds, it is possible for it to live out all year. However, even with a horse turned out all year, there are many things to consider. The quality and quantity of grass will vary throughout the year and, during the winter months, the horse will need hay and extra hard feed. In addition, it will probably require a New Zealand rug and access to a field shelter. These items are necessary if the animal is to stay in good condition during the winter months.

A horse turned out at grass, as well as a stabled horse turned out for even a few hours a day during the winter, must be checked for mud fever, rain scald and cuts.

In the spring and early summer, the grass grows furiously and you should constantly check your horse for any gain in weight. If you can, divide up your paddock so the grazing is alternated regularly.

A fly fringe affords protection in the summer.

The authors' own Mayhill Stud.
Good grazing and well maintained fencing are essential.

Perhaps a smaller paddock with little grass can made available, so your horse can be moved to this paddock if it is getting too fat. If your horse is allowed to become too overweight, firstly, it would be unfit and, secondly, a condition known as laminitis may develop.

Laminitis is an inflammation of the laminae in a horse's foot. When laminitis is present the horse is reluctant to move and stands with its hind legs well under it in an effort to take the weight off its front feet.

Treatment for laminitis involves moving the horse to a stable or starvation paddock and its diet will have to be severely restricted. Veterinary treatment is also required. Laminitis need never occur if you pay proper attention and care to the grass-kept horse.

A field shelter provides an escape from the wind and rain, and helps to keep the horse warm in winter. In summer it provides an escape from the persistent irritation of flies. It may also be necessary to fit a fly fringe to the horse's head collar in summer.

Allow for one acre per horse when considering the paddock size and there should be a good covering of meadow grass. The paddock can be fenced with post and rail fencing and a fresh water supply must always be available. Good grazing and a well-maintained paddock will help to keep your horse healthy. Regularly collect the droppings from the grass. Fertilising, spraying, rolling and topping the pasture is highly recommended to ensure that the paddock remains in good order.

Worming

Worming frequently is a very important part of maintaining a horse's health, particularly with the grass-kept horse.

All horses have worms, so regular worming is essential to control their number and prevent them from spreading throughout the horse's intestines. Worms live off the horse's food, thereby depriving the horse of its nutrients. They also invade the horse's blood vessels and are a very common cause of colic in horses. Their larvae migrating to major blood vessels can cause blockages and fatal haemorrhages. Horses become infected when grazing, through eating worm larvae hatched from eggs which have been deposited on the ground. Worms can live a long time inside a horse, so regular worming is essential and will reduce contamination of the field. Horses should be wormed every six weeks. Horses turned out together in the same paddock should be wormed simultaneously.

A wide variety of wormers is available. It is a good idea to alternate between several brands because worms can become immune to wormers with which they are familiar. It is also necessary to worm at least twice a year, in the spring and autumn, with a wormer that is effective in the control of bot worms (see chapter 2). Since wormers are also subject to change and development, it may be worth while taking veterinary advice as to which wormer will be most effective and the best time to dose.

Wormers are administered in either a paste contained in a syringe or by powder. In special cases a vet can administer them through a stomach tube.

Water

Horses should have an unlimited supply of water although they should not be given large amounts before, during or immediately

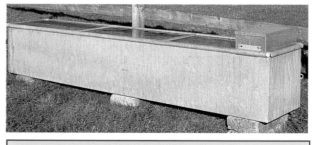

Horses which have been turned out should have access to fresh, clean water.

after exercise. It is preferable to water horses before feeding and after exercise. It is better to let them have smaller drinks with intervals between each session.

Hay

The grass-kept horse will almost certainly need hay in the winter months. Grass does not grow during this period and what there is contains little goodness. In extremely cold and snowy conditions, hay is the only food source available. A grass-kept horse maintained on very poor grazing in the summer may also require hay,

Try to feed only good quality hay. Well-made meadow hay may be best.

particularly if the weather has been very hot and dry and the grass has not grown.

The stabled horse needs hay all year round, fed in controlled amounts together with its hard feed. Problems do occur with hay, noticeably at the hay-making stage. The weather can have a dramatic effect on the quality of hay. Hay that has been baled too early and not allowed to dry can become mouldy and fusty.

Try to feed only good quality hay, for example, good, well-made meadow hay. You can get an idea of the quality by smelling the hay, which should have a sweet scent. Mouldy and dusty hay should be avoided at all times.

Even in good-quality hay, dust spores can be a problem and lead to coughs and respiratory problems. If your hay does seem a little dusty, you may try soaking it. Only do so for five minutes because over-soaked hay can ferment and cause colic.

There are alternatives to baled hay, such as Horsehage which is high in vitamins and completely dust-free. It is conveniently wrapped in polythene but can be a little expensive.

You should never feed big bale silage, as it may lead to botulism poisoning which can be fatal.

Teeth

Whether grass-kept or stabled, horses need to have their teeth looked after. They are an

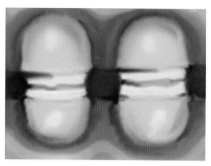

At birth the foal's milk teeth are covered in a fine membrane. The first teeth to erupt are the two central incisors and two or three molars.

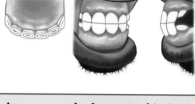

At one year, the four central incisors meet and the corner incisors can be clearly seen. The yearling's first permanent molars appear.

By two years old all the milk teeth are through. The young horse may begin to show signs of teething as the permanent teeth start to grow.

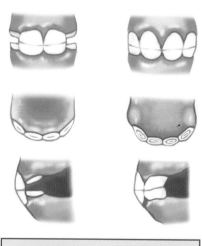

In the first five months the next incisors appear but it will be two or three months later before the corner incisors begin to show through the gum.

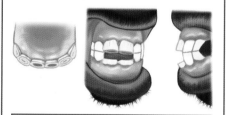

The first permanent incisors appear at two and a half years. The milk teeth loosen and fall out and the young horse has the gappy look of a human six year old.

By three years old the horse has two large, yellowish permanent incisors in both jaws, with white milk teeth beginning to loosen on either side.

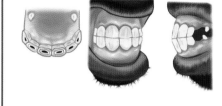

At five the horse has all twelve permanent incisors. Its mouth is distinguished from the two year old by the darkness of the 'marks' on the biting surface.

At three and a half years the last milk teeth are being replaced by permanent ones. In some male horses, the canine teeth or tushes on the lower jaw may appear.

At six it is getting quite difficult to tell the age of the horse. The marks on the two central incisors are now smaller than the rest.

The four year old has four permanent incisors in each jaw, their yellow colour contrasting with the corner incisors, which still have to be shed.

At seven the corner incisors are the only ones left with large marks. These teeth have developed a small projection at the rear - the seven-year-hook.

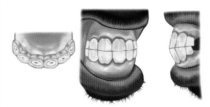

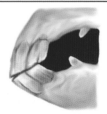

It is still possible at eight years old to tell the age accurately from the teeth. The marks are similar on all teeth and the seven-year-hook has disappeared.

The groove reaches the biting surface at about twenty and by twenty - five has almost gone. As the horse ages, the teeth become yellower, longer and more sloping.

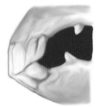

Galvayne's groove, a small furrow, appears at the top of the outer incisor at around ten years old. At fifteen it has reached about half way down the tooth.

The marks on a horse aged between twenty - five and thirty have faded, and the biting surface is no longer oval in shape. Galvayne's groove has disappeared completely.

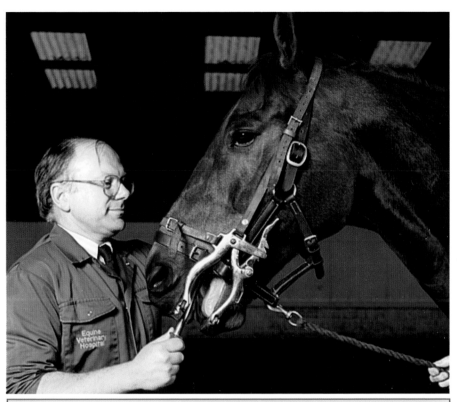

Vet Jeremy Mantell rasping teeth.
Note the use of a gag to ensure better access to the horse's mouth.

essential element in maintaining your horse's health. Unattended teeth can be painful, not only when eating but also if the horse is being ridden. In order to digest food properly, the horse must be able to break it down sufficiently and it needs level teeth to do this. Premolars and molars do not always wear evenly and sharp edges can form which cut into the horse's cheek. A horse's upper teeth are often closer to the front than the lower teeth. If this area is not worn, a hook can develop.

The above dental problems can lead to a cut and very sore mouth which is uncomfortable for the horse. When it is being ridden, the discomfort can make the horse hang on to the bit and not relax in the jaw. Any problems that you have with your horse's schooling may develop from its lack of acceptance of the bit. In such cases it is worth inspecting the mouth first to make sure that all is well.

Treatment would involve having your horse's teeth rasped. Rasping removes the

Preparing the foot.

Trimming.

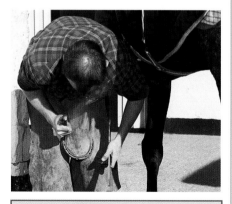

Bedding the hot shoe.

sharp edges, thus preventing cuts. The teeth will also be better able to break down the food, thus assisting the digestion process.

Teeth rasping can be carried out by your vet or horse dentist. Generally speaking, teeth should be rasped every six months. However, do check your horse's teeth as a matter of course if any problems arise.

Foot Care

The old saying 'No foot – no horse' is very true. The horse's feet are very sensitive and must be attended to regularly. Even if your horse is turned out, you should check and pick out its feet daily. The unshod horse will also need its feet trimmed, as uneven wear causes the feet to change shape. Regular rasping and trimming prevent this. Trimming is also necessary to preserve the correct angle of the foot in relation to the ground. A horse without shoes may wear out its toes and its heels will continue to grow. You should pay particular attention to the heel. If too much is trimmed the horse's heel will collapse and the horse will walk with more weight on its heel. This can be a factor in the development of more severe conditions such as navicular disease (see chapter 2).

The feet of a stabled horse should be regularly cleaned out to prevent thrush developing (see chapter 2).

Shoeing

The interval between shoeing differs with each horse. The wear rate of shoes is

The horse's feet are very sensitive and must be attended to regularly.

influenced by the amount of exercise the horse has and the type of surface it moves on. Hoof growth rate is also variable. On average, shoes need to be removed and the feet trimmed every four to six weeks regardless of whether the shoes have worn out. The horse requires shoes when either they have become loose, the clenches have risen or the feet have become noticeably long. If shoes are left on too long, the outer wall of the hoof may grow around the shoe, most usually at the heel. This causes pressure on the sole of the foot and is a common cause of corns.

Chapter Two

Common ailments

 This book cannot cover every equine illness or disease in detail, but the following are the ones you should be aware of. If ever you are in doubt about the health of your horse, do not hesitate to contact a veterinary surgeon.

Equine Flu

Symptoms include a hard, dry cough and a watery discharge from the nose which may become very thick. The horse may also suffer from a high fever, a loss of appetite and energy and be generally depressed. Veterinary treatment is essential. The horse will also need lots of fresh air and rest.

Equine influenza is highly infectious and can sweep through a stable yard. It can cause lung and heart problems, and permanently damage the horse's health, Immunisation is not 100 per cent effective, although a horse that catches the disease following vaccination tends to suffer much milder symptoms. Vaccination requires two initial doses (administered four to six weeks apart) which is followed by a third injection six months later. Annual boosters should then follow.

In an effort to reduce the outbreaks of equine flu, many show organisers now require confirmation of vaccination to accompany an entry into their competitions. If you do intend to compete within organisations such as the British Horse Society (BHS) or the British Show Jumping Association (BSJA), do keep your horse vaccination certificates up to date. Failure to produce these may mean you are banned from such events.

Tetanus

Tetanus is caused by an organism that lives in the ground and in droppings. If the horse becomes infected, perhaps through a puncture wound, its body will go rigid, it will have difficulty in eating and chewing and it will drool.

All horses should be vaccinated regularly against tetanus. If a horse receives a cut it can be injected against tetanus, but the protection only lasts a few weeks. As horses seem to have a talent for injuring themselves on a fairly regular basis, it it worth having them vaccinated. As with equine flu, two injections are administered four to six weeks apart, followed by an annual booster. You will find that from a financial point of view it is probably better to have the flu and tetanus injections done together.

Colic

This is one of the most common illnesses in the horse. Colic is an abdominal pain.

The signs are: loss of appetite and a lethargic appearance. The horse may look around at its flanks and paw at the ground. As the pain intensifies, the horse wants to lie down and roll, in a vain attempt to relieve the pain. Unfortunately, being allowed to roll may lead to an even more serious situation known as twisted gut. The horse may also start to sweat.

Any of these signs indicate the onset of colic and the sooner a vet is called the better. In most cases the vet will administer a pain-killing injection and relief will occur fairly quickly. If you believe your horse has colic, keep it warm and, if possible, walk it quietly around until veterinary assistance arrives.

A twisted gut can be only be rectified by surgery. Surgery on twisted guts does seem to have become more successful in recent times. The chances of a good recovery often depends on how quickly the problem is diagnosed and treated. Twisted gut can be difficult to diagnose at first and usually becomes more apparent after the failure of the horse to respond to pain killers.

Although colic can be brought on by incorrect feeding and, sometimes, stress, the

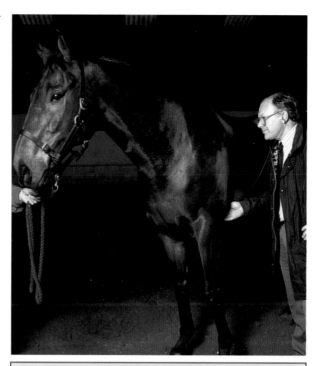

Checking the pulse.

most common cause is damage caused by worms.

Colic that comes on suddenly, where the horse not only displays the usual signs but has rapid breathing and a raised pulse which appears, subsides and returns a few hours later, is called spasmodic colic. Treatment with pain killers may have to be repeated although modern drugs are extremely effective.

Flatulent colic is formed by fermentation in the stomach or intestines. The bowels become distended, causing pain. This colic often occurs from overeating, or perhaps from eating the wrong type of food such as grass cuttings, which should always be avoided. This colic can be identified by the gurgling sound which emanates from the horse's stomach. Pain killers should be administered and, in some cases, a stomach tube will be used to relieve gases from the stomach.

Another type of colic is known as impacted colic. This occurs when the muscle contraction that moves the food along the digestive system slows down due to a lack of fluid passing through the intestines. The bowel contents have trouble passing through the system and a blockage occurs. This situation seems to be more common in stabled horses and may be a result of feeding large amounts of dry food such as hay and concentrates. Contributory factors can be the horse drinking insufficient water coupled with lack of exercise. Adding salt or a laxative such as Epsom Salts to the horse's diet will help to increase the horse's water intake. Treatment may involve administering liquid paraffin and an agent to stimulate gut movement through a stomach tube. Pain-killing drugs will also be necessary to keep the horse out of pain while the impaction is clearing.

Azotoria

One thing that many people forget is to decrease or increase the amount of hard feed a horse has in respect of the amount of work it is doing. Obviously, if under-fed and over-worked, the horse's body will not cope. It loses weight and its coat looks dull. These are the visible signs, although they should never be allowed to happen. Feeding too much and not working enough can induce a condition known as azotoria. Classically, the problem occurs soon after exercise. The signs vary from a mild stiffness of the hind limbs to an apparent seizure of all the limbs. The horse sweats, shows great reluctance to move, and is obviously in pain. The muscles of the back and hindquarters may feel unusually firm. Veterinary assistance is required in the short term. The horse's rations need to be severely reduced. Some horses make a complete recovery, never to experience the problem again. However, once a horse has had azotoria, the chances of it recurring do seem to increase.

Even if overfeeding does not lead to the critical stages of azotoria, it could result in the horse being very excitable to ride and handle, which creates problems of its own. Always pay great attention to the horse's feeding pattern and remember to feed according to the degree of work your horse is doing.

Navicular disease

Navicular disease occurs almost exclusively in a horse's front feet. Usually both feet are affected and you will notice that the horse shortens its stride and may be reluctant to go forward correctly, especially at the trot. This may be more noticeable on hard ground. Another sign may be that the horse points its toe on one or both legs. Although horses with all types of foot conformation can get

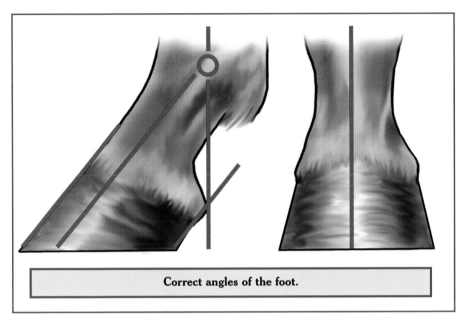

Correct angles of the foot.

the disease, those which have an incorrect foot, such as long toes and collapsed heels, seem to have a higher incidence rate.

A well-balanced foot is one where the weight is evenly distributed over the whole foot. The ground-bearing surface should be level. The front foot, wall of the hoof, the pastern and slope of the heel should be at an angle of 45° to the horizontal. The hind feet are generally steeper, having a hoof pastern axis of 50–55°.

Bot fly

Bot worms originate from bot flies, which look very much like bees. The bot flies attach their eggs to the hairs on the horse's forelegs, neck and shoulder. The eggs are easily identified by their yellow colour. When the horse licks or bites its body, the larvae attach themselves to its mouth. The larvae burrow into the horse's gums and stay there for about a month until they are swallowed. From here they attach to the stomach wall. The larvae spend nine months in total in the horse, at the end of which time they are passed in the horse's droppings. To help prevent the larvae from making their way to the horse's mouth, remove the eggs and larvae from the legs with a purpose-made knife.

Thrush

Thrush occurs if the horse's feet are allowed to become clogged with droppings and absorb moisture from a dirty stable. The foot appears to be soft, particularly in the frog area and there is usually a rather unpleasant smell. Some horses contract thrush because they have very deep clefts alongside their frogs which may be difficult to clean. If this situation develops even though you have been cleaning out your horse's feet regularly, a mild solution of hydrogen peroxide dispensed from a syringe to the affected area usually clears things up fairly quickly.

Mud fever

This condition is found on the legs. The affected areas constitute a swelling with the serum seeping through the skin and, eventually, through cracks in the skin. Treatment for a grass-kept horse means moving it into drier conditions. Remove any excess hair around the affected area and make sure it is clean and dry. A diluted iodine solution is the most effective cleaning agent. However, you should also seek veterinary advice.

Rain scald

Rain scald can occur when the horse's skin is saturated by prolonged rain. Lesions are found on the back, belly and lower limbs. The hair appears matted, with tufts. When you pull the tufts gently, they will come away, leaving a gray-coloured pus stuck to them. The horse's back will be very sore. Keep the horse in and remove the hair from the affected area. Wash the horse's back. Antibiotics will probably have to be administered by the vet.

The horse turned out at grass should be checked at least twice a day. As well as looking for the development of the above skin infections, examine it for any cuts and pick its feet out.

Wounds and Treatment

Wounds of one sort or another are very common in horses. They usually occur as the result of being kicked or bitten, becoming entangled in fencing or, perhaps, through competitive work.

Open wounds can become contaminated by bacteria which, when established, infect the wound. Hosing is the best way to clean many wounds initially, especially if they are dirty or covered with mud. Surrounding areas should also be hosed clean in preparation for applying a dressing.

Some wounds do not require bandaging due to their size or perhaps their position, such as a wound on the upper body. Some wounds are better left open, but kept clean and free from dirt. These wounds can be treated either with a wound powder or an antibiotic spray. Some leg wounds, however, may need to be bandaged.

Wounds of this nature should be thoroughly cleansed and dressed with a non-adhesive dressing which is either sterile or at least very clean. Use padding such as cotton wool or gamgee to help distribute the pressure of the bandage and also to absorb any discharge. The padding should be impregnated with a wound dressing. Generally a petroleum or antibiotic dressing should be applied to wounds that require bandaging. Many suitable dressings can be purchased from outlets such as saddlers. Depending on the nature of the cut, the dressing can be held in place either by a crepe bandage or stable bandage, or it may be necessary to use an adhesive bandage. Take great care not to apply the bandage too tightly as it could interfere with the blood circulation to the area.

Lower leg wounds below the knee or hock are relatively straightforward, but pay particular attention to any bandage that is required over the knee. You should never bandage over the small bony area behind the knee since the bending action of the knee would make the bandage rub, causing a sore place.

When bandaging a damaged leg one very important consideration is to remember to also bandage the opposite good leg. The reason is that when a horse has a damaged leg it places more weight and, consequently, more strain on the good leg. It is not uncommon for a horse to end up with a damaged 'good' leg.

A common cause of lameness is a puncture or bruising to the sole of the foot which has become infected. This is not always easy to detect and in most cases it is usually discovered by the vet on inspection of the hoof. If the foot is pinched with callipers the horse reacts to a sore area. If the vet suspects the presence of a small puncture that may contain trapped pus, he will gradually cut into the foot with a hoof knife and expose the problem. Opening the

area usually releases the trapped pus. However, not everything will come out and the foot will have to be poulticed for a few days to remove any further poison.

The most widely-used poultice is Animalintex. This is an impregnated wool pad which you soak in warm water and apply to the affected area. It can be bandaged into place with a sticky bandage which holds it quite firmly. It may also be necessary for you to place an equiboot over the bandage to keep everything in place. You may have to replace the poultice twice a day and, on examination, you will see the pus drawn from the affected area on the Animalintex. You should continue poulticing until there is no evidence of infection left in the area.

Signs of Illness

Signs of ill health can be detected in many ways. The experienced person notices changes in the horse's condition and behaviour. To the inexperienced these may be difficult to observe early on, when treatment would be most effective.

Changes in appearance may include:
- the condition of the horse's coat, which may become dull
- any swelling or enlargements of limbs
- behavioural changes such as loss of energy or appetite
- any abnormal body function such as a change in the passing of urine or droppings.

The loss of appetite is perhaps the most reliable and obvious sign that something is wrong. Weight loss over a period of time suggests that either the horse is not receiving enough food or it is not gaining enough nutrition from what it is eating. In this situation, have its teeth checked and a worm count carried out by a vet. This will show any worm infestation, which can be treated accordingly.

A grass-kept horse may lose condition in the winter even if it is being fed large amounts of food. If there are no dental or worm problems, it may be suffering from the cold. Rug the horse up with a New Zealand rug to offer protection from the cold and rain.

When a horse is unwell and has a temperature it is important to keep it warm. It needs to be stabled and rugged up; wrap stable bandages around the legs as these will also help to keep it warm.

Stable bandages are usually made of wool and should be placed over the top of a roll of cotton wool or gamgee. The bandages should be applied to the leg from just below the knee to the coronet. The tape fastenings should be done up on the outside of the leg, not at the front or back where they may cause pressure to build up. The bandages should be done up firmly but not too tightly.

First Aid Box

All stable yards and all horse owners should have a First Aid Box big enough to take with you to shows or whenever you travel with your horse. The First Aid Box should contain at least two elastic or crepe bandages, two elastoplast rolls, a roll of cotton wool or gamgee, an antibiotic spray, wound powder, cleaning agent, thermometer, Animalintex and a pair of scissors. A First Aid box of this nature contains the basic materials to deal with an emergency.

The stable

The ideal stable should be warm, very well-drained and draught-free. It must also be adequately ventilated, of course.

A poorly-ventilated stable generally smells, no matter how clean you keep it. In addition, the horse needs clean, fresh air in order to breathe properly. The walls should be smooth with no protruding or dangerous obstacles that might cause injury. Ideally the box should be roughly 4.25m x 3.65m (14ft x 12ft) in size, with a ceiling about 3m (10ft) high. Floor areas should have a roughened surface to prevent the horse slipping, and electricity and a fresh water supply should be available.

Stable windows should be operational but must be covered by a metal grill to prevent injury. Windows should be on the same side as the door to prevent draughts. Hide any electric cables and make sure any switches are out of reach of the horse. Light bulbs should be covered by a wire mesh grill unless they are well out of reach of the horse. Make sure that the lighting is well away from any hay so that the hay does not come into contact with a hot bulb.

Relaxing in a comfortable bed.

Chapter Three

It is preferable to have the stable as uncluttered as possible, regarding fixtures and fittings. The more objects there are hanging on the wall, the greater the chance of the horse injuring itself. The one fixture that is required is a tie ring. This should be placed roughly 1.5m (5ft) from the ground. As well as tying up the horse, you may use it to hang a haynet and this will be sufficiently high to do so safely.

Bedding Materials

Straw is perhaps the bedding material favoured by most horse owners, and it is definitely the cheapest. If enough is used, straw also provides a warm, deep bed for the horse to lie down on. Wheat straw is perhaps the favourite. Oat and barley straw is quite palatable and, as a result, horses tend to eat large amounts of it, although some horses are also partial to wheat straw. As with hay, dirty or mouldy straw can lead to respiratory problems. If your horse is stabled on wheat straw and you are having a problem with it eating its bed, spray a weak solution of disinfectant on the new straw which may prevent the horse from eating it.

For most horses in competitive work or training, paper or shavings are a more sensible choice. As well as removing the likelihood of allergic reactions, you can feed and hay your horse knowing that it is not eating half a bale of straw a day as well.

Paper is best for any horse with a allergic reaction because it is virtually dust free, although it can prove expensive.

Shavings are probably more popular than paper, although do make sure that you only purchase white wood shavings. When in contact with the horse's urine, red wood shavings can release acids which are bad for horse's feet.

Stable Routine

It is important to establish a routine for the stable horse. Horses are creatures of habit and they come to expect attention, exercise and feeding at the same time each day. The stable routine includes mucking out, turning out, exercising and grooming, and good stable management will also include making time for cleaning tack.

Listed below is a rough guide. Although it may not be possible to keep rigidly to this, feeds should be given at the same time each day.

A typical stable routine is as follows:	
6.45	Feed
7.15	Muck out
9.00	Exercise
10.30	Turn out (skip out stable)
1.00	Back in stable (small feed and hay depending on horse's work, amounts will vary)
2.00	Grooming
	Tack cleaning
4.15	Muck out
4.30	Hay
5.00	Feed

The horse's metabolism becomes used to being given food at the same time each day. If that suddenly changes, the animal becomes upset and worried. If the horse starts to become concerned, it may start banging its door and develop stable vices such as weaving crib biting and wind sucking.

The stabled horse should be fed two or three times a day, interspersed with controlled amounts of hay. The quantity of hard feed depends on the type of horse and the work it is doing. Feeding has been made much easier in recent times as prepared mixes of feed containing all the right nutrients that the horse requires on a daily basis are now widely available. Some provide a maintenance diet for horses resting or on very light work. Competition mixes provide more energy for the horse in hard work or competition work.

With a new horse you may have to experiment to see what is best both for it and for you. If you want to change a horse's diet to any great degree, do this gradually. Introduce a little of the new type of feed each day, and this allows the horse's digestive system to adjust to the change of diet.

Mucking out one horse on straw usually takes about 15 minutes. Deep litter bedding, where you take out the majority of muck but then add straw to the rest, does save time. However, this method of mucking out means that every few weeks you need to clean the stable right out. In addition, there

will be a build up of ammonia and fungal spores, which is not very healthy and does not help a horse with an allergic reaction. Generally, it is better to clean the stable out by placing the clean straw on one side, removing all the muck, sweeping out the floor and then replacing the bed.

Allow at least two hours for your horse to digest its food before exercising.

Exercise should be varied but obviously depends on what you are doing with your horse, from gentle hacks to preparing it for a competition. The duration of the exercise is also variable, according to your aims, although a healthy horse should have a minimum of an hour a day.

When exercising, always protect your horse's legs with tendon boots. Knee boots are also advisable in case it should fall on the road.

All stabled horses should be able to go out as often as possible, grazing and weather permitting.

The amount of turnout your horse has is again determined by what you are doing with it. A general riding horse may not need to be as fit as a competition horse, and the amount of food it consumes may not be so important. However, a horse in training may have to have its grazing monitored in terms of how much weight it is carrying, the time of year and its temperament.

Most stabled horses enjoy being turned out. However, when it is wet and cold, you may find that older horses are only too happy to return to their own stables. Longer

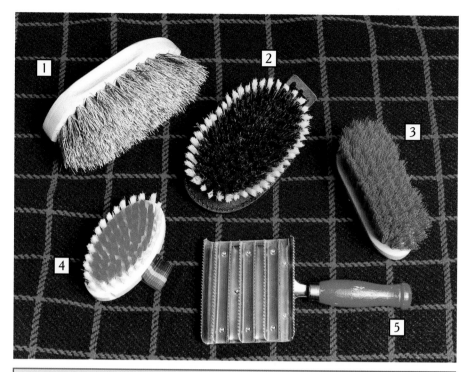

1. Dandy Brush. 2. Large Body Brush. 3. Water Brush. 4. Small Body Brush. 5. Metal Curry Comb.

periods of turnout may benefit some horses, such as those with nervous dispositions who will be more relaxed with more turnout. So turnout is very much an individual concern. You need to experiment with your horse's turnout to establish what is best for it and also works for you.

Grooming

Your horse should be groomed every day as part of your stable routine. Grooming keeps its coat clean and helps to promote a healthy shine. This is also an ideal time to check thoroughly all over your horse's body for minor cuts, abrasions or skin irritations. Checking the feet, oiling the hooves and pulling and trimming the mane and tail are all parts of grooming.

Before exercise brush off your horse, paying particular attention to the areas under the saddle and the girth area. Brush out the mane and tail with a soft body brush. Use damp sponges to remove any dirt around the eyes and nostrils.

A more thorough grooming can be carried out after the horse has been exercised and turned out. First check the feet, picking them out to make sure that all the stones and

Regular grooming is an essential part of the horse's daily routine.

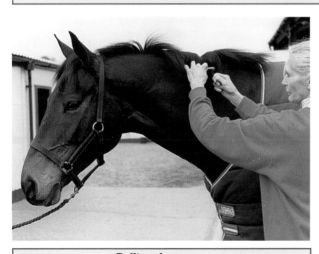

Pulling the mane.

grit have been removed from the sides of the frog and under the rim of the shoes. Next, remove any mud with the dandy brush, although the dandy brush should not be used on sensitive areas such as the stomach, back or head. The body brush, as the name suggests, is much softer and is used to clean the horse thoroughly all over. The body brush is used in a circular motion and every now and then should be cleaned with a metal curry comb. To finish, go over the horse with a slightly dampened stable cloth to remove any remaining dirt.

Mane and Tail Pulling

Use the mane comb when you do the mane and tail pulling. When the horse's mane requires pulling, comb it through thoroughly, removing any tangles or matted hair. Start by pulling the longer hairs; take a few hairs at a time from underneath the mane and, gradually, you will see the mane becoming thinner and shorter. Continue along the mane until you have achieved the required length. If the horse objects you may be trying to pull too much hair at once.

Tail pulling is carried out in a similar way.

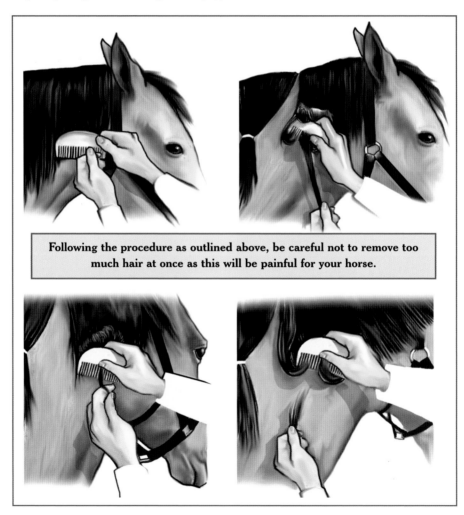

Following the procedure as outlined above, be careful not to remove too much hair at once as this will be painful for your horse.

The hairs around the top of the tail tend to become thick and require thinning. Only take the hair from the sides. Begin at the top and work down, again removing only a very few hairs at one time. Pay particular attention to the horse's reaction when the tail is being pulled as some horses have quite sensitive tails. Always stand to one side when pulling and, if necessary, have someone hold the horse in the stable and pull its tail from behind the door. Although this may be a little restrictive, it is better than being kicked.

Clipping

During summer the horse's coat thins out and is quite easy to maintain. As the autumn approaches the coat begins to thicken.

As with the mane, remove only small amounts of hair at a time, taken from the roots to keep the tail neat and tidy.

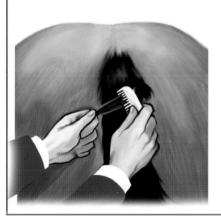

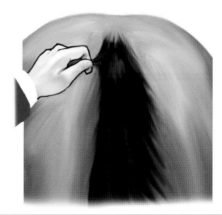

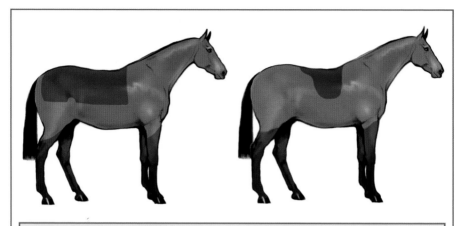

Left to right: Blanket clip. Hunter clip.

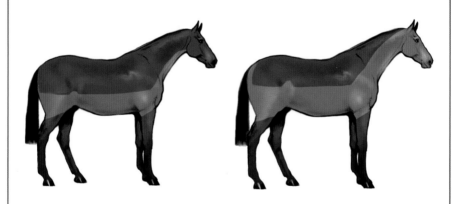

Left to right: Low trace. High trace.

If the horse is to remain in work it will need clipping. The type of clip depends on the work you will be doing. If the horse is doing very light work, a trace clip is adequate. This clip removes the hair from the areas that get particularly sweaty and muddy and make the horse easier to keep clean.

A blanket clip, as the name suggests, leaves the hair on the horse roughly in the area that a rug would cover. This is a suitable clip for a stabled horse in medium work.

The full clip is where all the hair is removed. This clip is suitable for horses in heavy work, such as racehorses. A full clip, where the legs and saddle area are left unclipped, is known as a hunter clip.

If you are clipping for the first time, and perhaps it is a new experience for your horse as well, turn on the clippers and let the horse become accustomed to the noise before you attempt to remove any coat. It is better to start clipping the horse away from its head.

Cut the coat in the opposite direction to its lay. When clipping, always maintain an even pressure on the clippers and pay be careful around the sensitive areas on the horse's body. Extra care should be taken around the eyes and ears.

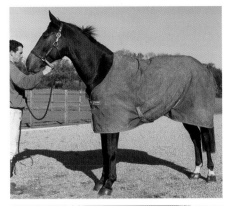

Rugs and Rugging

You need a variety of rugs for your horse, how many and of what type again depend on where and how you keep it.

If your horse is turned out full time, then it may not require a rug at all. However, when the weather turns particularly bad it is advisable for the horse to wear a New Zealand rug. This will protect it from the elements and prevent it losing condition. The stabled horse requires a selection of rugs. These are: a day rug (a blanket or a quilted under rug can be added for extra warmth), a travelling rug and a night rug (jute or heavy quilted material). Most rugs now have fastening straps which run under the horse's stomach and do up on the side. Generally, these are considered better for the horse's back than using a heavy roller to hold the rugs in place.

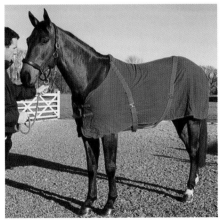

**From top to bottom:
New Zealand rug.
Stable rug and blanket.
Summer sheet.**

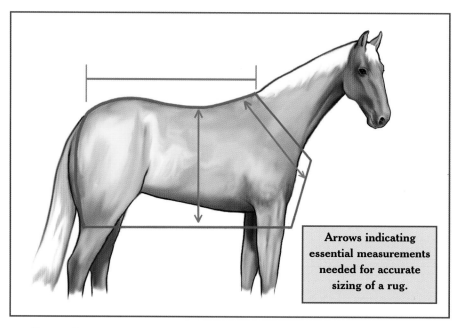

Arrows indicating essential measurements needed for accurate sizing of a rug.

During the day, the horse may need a summer sheet, perhaps together with the blanket depending on its clip and the weather, with the heavy quilted night rug replaced by a lighter day rug. After heavy exercise or being washed down the horse will require a sweat sheet. These are designed to allow the coat to breathe whilst still keeping the horse warm. Use one with large perforations in summer and a slightly heavier rug with smaller perforations in colder conditions. In general it is better to have two of everything; in particular a second New Zealand Rug will be especially beneficial when the conditions are very wet. Good horse husbandry also requires your horse to have clean, well maintained rugs.

In Conclusion

To care for your horse, you must be prepared to spend time, energy and money on it. You cannot leave it out in its field for weeks on end and expect it to behave perfectly the next time you decide to ride it. You cannot expect it to be healthy if it is living on poor grazing or in unhygienic conditions. When you bought your horse, you took on a responsibility for a living creature. Treat it well and you will be rewarded with many hours of companionship and fun.

Glossary

Azatoria	-	A locking or seizure of the horse's limbs
Clenches	-	Nail tips which hold the shoe onto the horse's foot
Clipping	-	Removal of the winter coat
Colic	-	An abdominal pain
Crib biting	-	The chewing of wood or the stable interior
Equine flu	-	A highly contagious disease; comparable to human influenza though, perhaps, worse since permanent damage to the horse's health can result
Gamgee	-	A cotton wool-like padding
Lameness	-	An uneven action in the horse's movement
Mud fever	-	A soreness which develops on the horse's legs
Navicular disease	-	A condition that affects the feet causing extreme pain and lameness. Almost exclusively found in the front feet.
Rain scald	-	Sores which appear on the body, caused by the skin becoming saturated with water during prolonged rain
Teeth rasping	-	The filing or rasping down of teeth to eliminate sharp edges
Thrush	-	A condition in which the feet become soft at the sides of the frog. Usually accompanied by a rotten unpleasant smell
Weaving	-	A condition where the horse stands and swings his head from side to side, usually when in his stable
Wind sucking	-	A condition where a horse will grab hold of the top of a stable door or any similar surface, tense his muscles and appear to suck in air
Worms	-	Internal parasites which attack the horse's intestines

Index